# Short**Flute**Pieces

Arranged by Hywel Davies

**Chester Music**
part of The Music Sales Group
London/New York/Paris/Sydney/Copenhagen/Berlin/Madrid/Tokyo

Compilation by Michael Ahmad.
Music Engraved by Camden Music.
Printed in the United Kingdom.

(*SARABANDE arranged by Alan Poulton)

# Alfie

Words by Hal David
Music by Burt Bacharach

# All I Ask Of You

from 'The Phantom Of The Opera'

Words by Charles Hart
Music by Andrew Lloyd Webber

# Annie's Song

Words & Music by John Denver

# Barcarolle

from 'The Tales Of Hoffmann'

Music by Jacques Offenbach

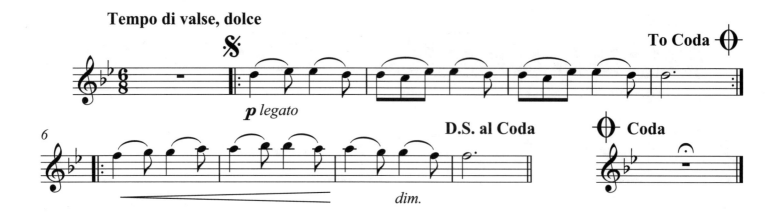

# El Condor Pasa (If I Could)

Traditional

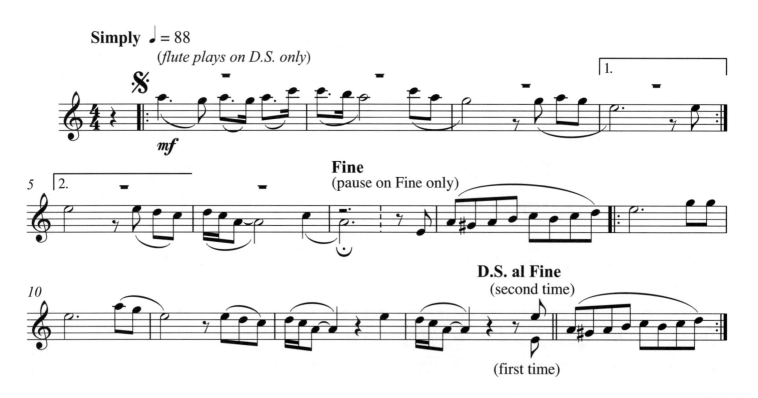

# Beautiful

Words & Music by Linda Perry

# Berceuse

### from 'Dolly Suite'

Music by Gabriel Fauré

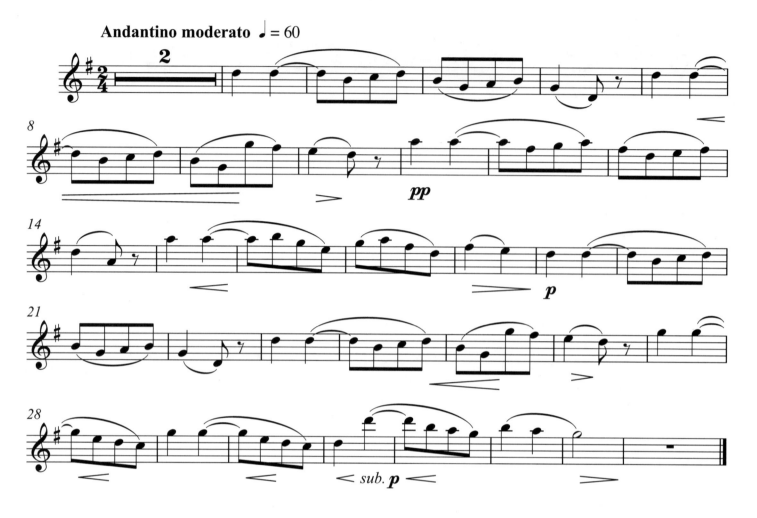

# Danny Boy (Londonderry Air)

Words by Fred E. Weatherly
Traditional Irish Melody

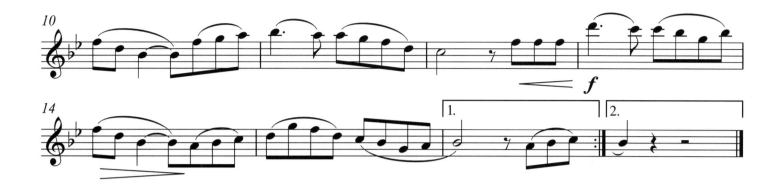

# Fly Me To The Moon (In Other Words)

Words & Music by Bart Howard

# Frosty The Snowman

Words & Music by
Steve Nelson & Jack Rollins

# Mad World

### from 'Donnie Darko'

Words & Music by Roland Orzabal

# Half The World Away

from 'The Royle Family'

Words & Music by Noel Gallagher

# Hopelessly Devoted To You

from 'Grease'

Words & Music by John Farrar

**Torch-holding ballad** ♩. = 84

# I Don't Want To Wait

from 'Dawson's Creek'

Words & Music by Paula Cole

# Into The West

from 'The Lord Of The Rings:
The Return Of The King'

Words & Music by Annie Lennox,
Howard Shore & Fran Walsh

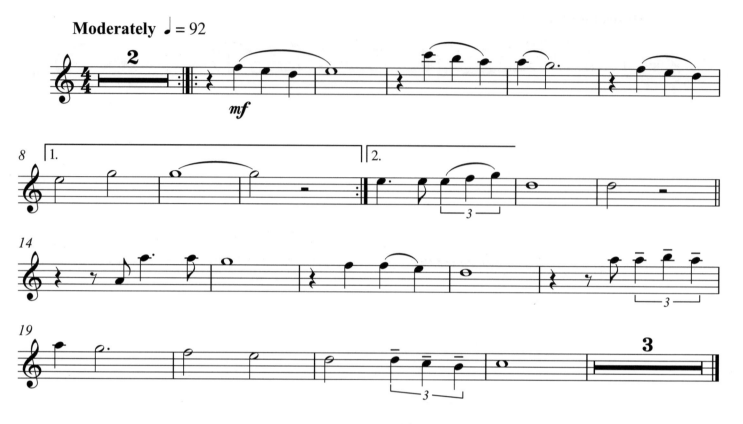

# Let It Snow! Let It Snow! Let It Snow!

Words by Sammy Cahn
Music by Jule Styne

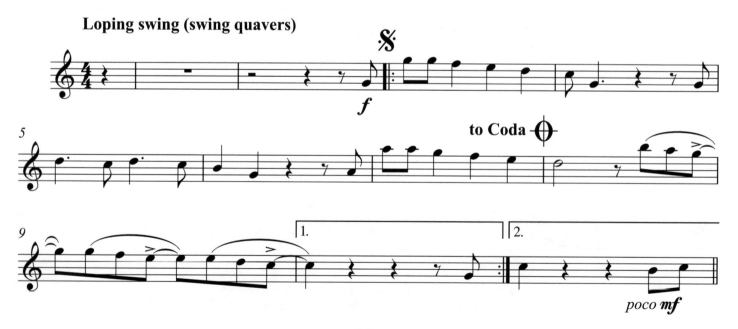

# Menuet

## from 'Suite No.2'

Johann Sebastian Bach

# Moon River

from 'Breakfast At Tiffany's'

Words by Johnny Mercer
Music by Henry Mancini

**Gently lilting**

# My Favourite Things

from 'The Sound Of Music'

Words by Oscar Hammerstein II
Music by Richard Rodgers

# The Odd Couple

Music by Neal Hefti

# Papageno's Song

from 'The Magic Flute'

Wolfgang Amadeus Mozart

**Andante**

# Sarabande

## from 'Solitaire'

Malcolm Arnold
arranged by Alan Poulton

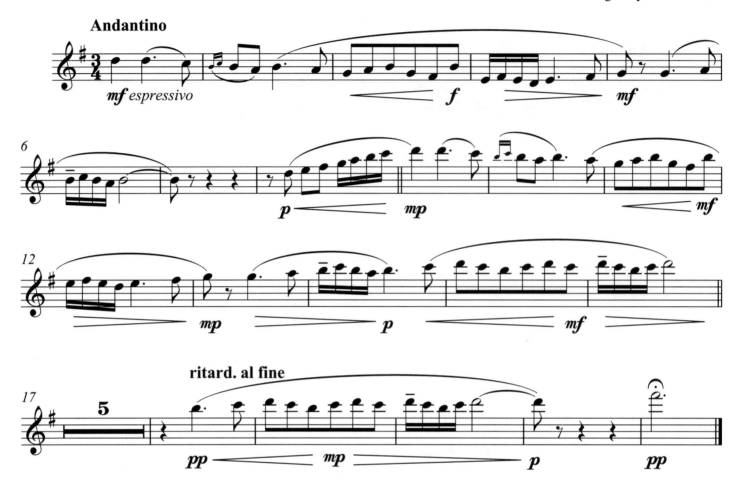

This arrangement is an abridged version of a larger flute and piano arrangement by Alan Poulton
(Order Number NOV954239)

# Somewhere Only We Know

Words & Music by Tim Rice-Oxley,
Tom Chaplin & Richard Hughes

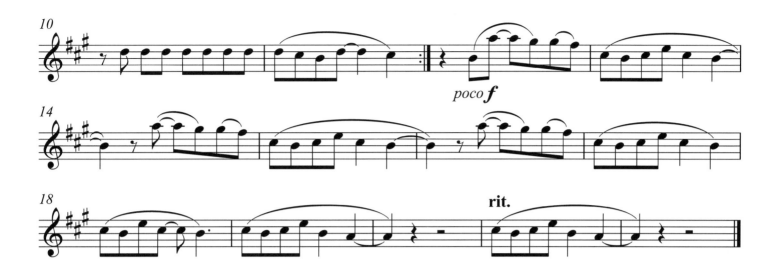

# To A Wild Rose

Music by Edward MacDowell

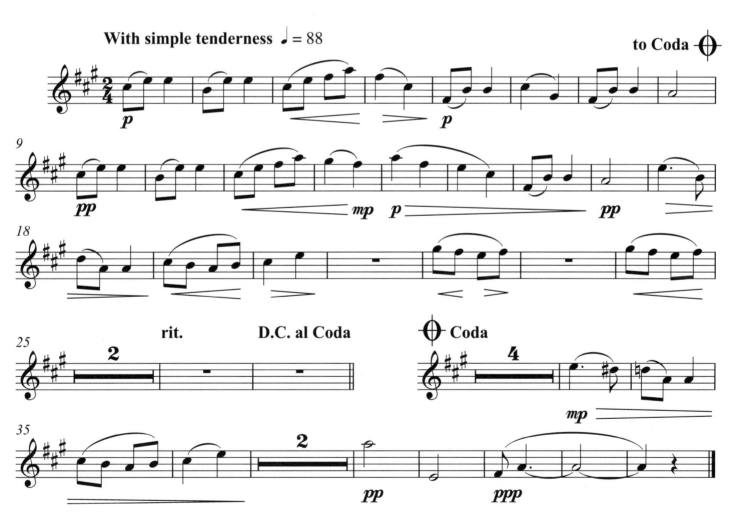

# We Wish You A Merry Christmas

Traditional

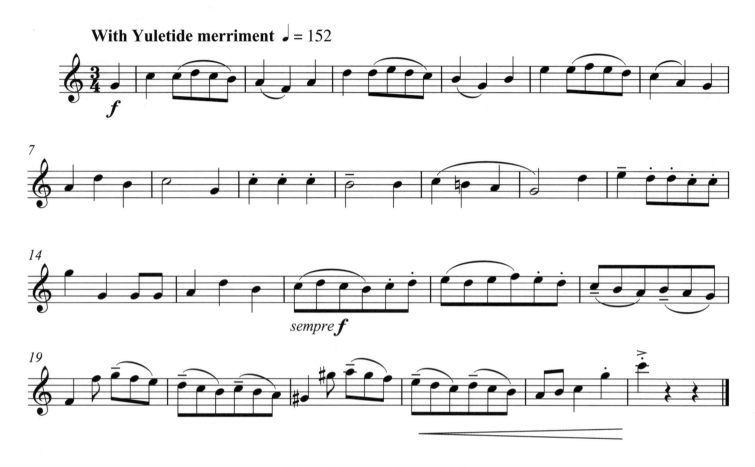

# Pavane

Music by Gabriel Fauré

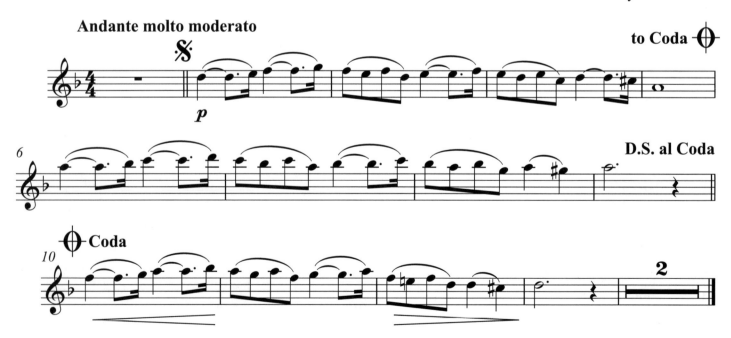

# Short **Flute** Pieces

Arranged by Hywel Davies
(*SARABANDE arranged by Alan Poulton)

Chester Music
part of The Music Sales Group
London/New York/Paris/Sydney/Copenhagen/Berlin/Madrid/Tokyo

Published by:
Chester Music Limited,
8/9 Frith Street, London, W1D 3JB, England.

Exclusive Distributors:
Music Sales Limited,
Distribution Centre, Newmarket Road, Bury St Edmunds, Suffolk, IP33 3YB, England.
Music Sales Pty Limited,
120 Rothschild Avenue, Rosebery, NSW 2018, Australia.

Order No. CH68717
ISBN 1-84449-604-X
This book © Copyright 2004 Chester Music.

Compilation by Michael Ahmad.
Music Engraved by Camden Music.
Printed in the United Kingdom.

Your Guarantee of Quality:
As publishers, we strive to produce every book to the highest commercial standards.
This book has been freshly engraved and avoids awkward page turns making playing from it a real pleasure.
Particular care has been given to specifying acid-free, neutral-sized paper made from
pulps which have not been elemental chlorine bleached.
The pulp is from farmed sustainable forests and was produced with special regard for the environment.
Throughout, the printing and binding have been planned to ensure a sturdy,
attractive publication which should give years of enjoyment.
If your copy fails to meet our high standards, please inform us and we will gladly replace it.

**www.musicsales.com**

# Alfie

Words by Hal David
Music by Burt Bacharach

# All I Ask Of You

## from 'The Phantom Of The Opera'

Words by Charles Hart
Music by Andrew Lloyd Webber

# Annie's Song

Words & Music by John Denver

# Barcarolle

## from 'The Tales Of Hoffmann'

Music by Jacques Offenbach

**Tempo di valse, dolce**

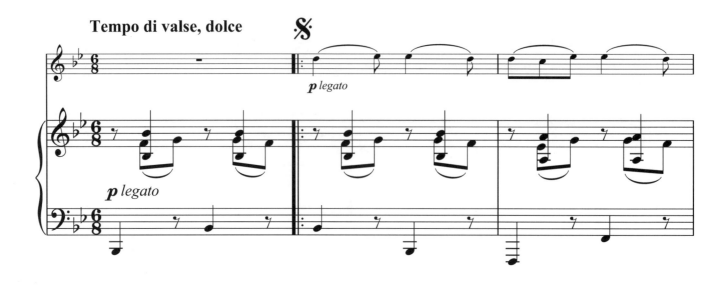

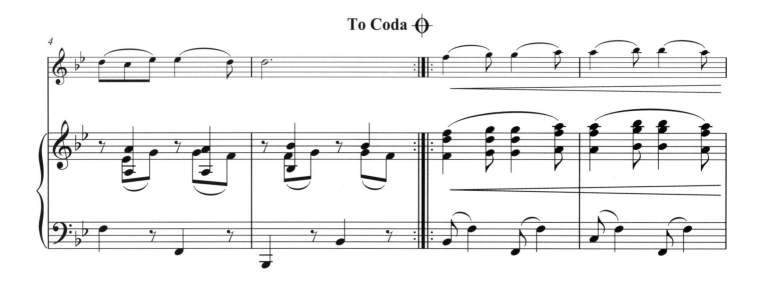

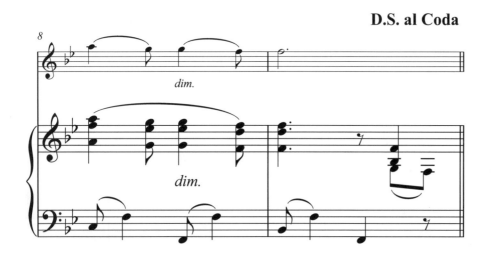

# El Condor Pasa (If I Could)

Traditional

# Beautiful

Words & Music by Linda Perry

**Tenderly** ♩ = 76

# Berceuse

from 'Dolly Suite'

Music by Gabriel Fauré

# Danny Boy (Londonderry Air)

Words by Fred E. Weatherly
Traditional Irish Melody

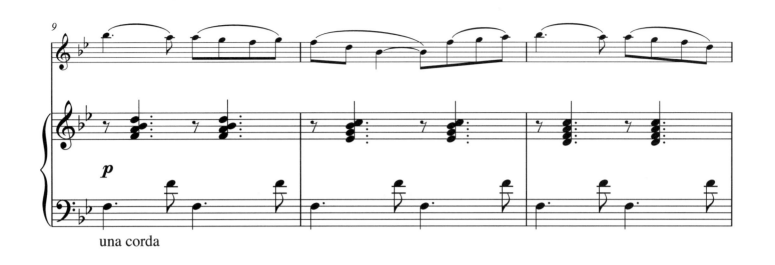

una corda

tre corde

# Fly Me To The Moon (In Other Words)

Words & Music by Bart Howard

# Frosty The Snowman

Words & Music by
Steve Nelson & Jack Rollins

**Brightly**

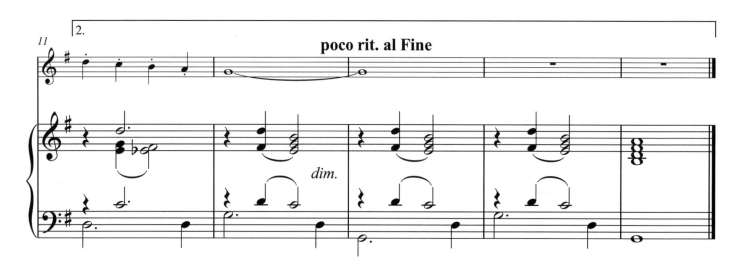

# Mad World

from 'Donnie Darko'

Words & Music by Roland Orzabal

# Half The World Away

from 'The Royle Family'

Words & Music by Noel Gallagher

# Hopelessly Devoted To You

from 'Grease'

Words & Music by John Farrar

23

# I Don't Want To Wait

from 'Dawson's Creek'

Words & Music by Paula Cole

**Moderately**

♩ = 92

# Into The West

from 'The Lord Of The Rings:
The Return Of The King'

Words & Music by Annie Lennox,
Howard Shore & Fran Walsh

Moderately ♩ = 92

26

# Let It Snow! Let It Snow! Let It Snow!

Words by Sammy Cahn
Music by Jule Styne

**Loping swing (swing quavers)**

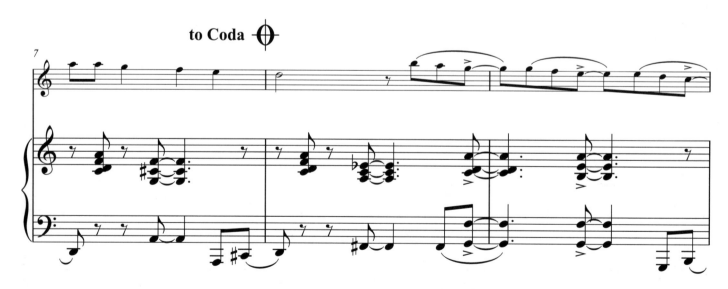

# Menuet

from 'Suite No.2'

Johann Sebastian Bach

# Moon River

from 'Breakfast At Tiffany's'

Words by Johnny Mercer
Music by Henry Mancini

**Gently lilting**

# My Favourite Things

from 'The Sound Of Music'

Words by Oscar Hammerstein II
Music by Richard Rodgers

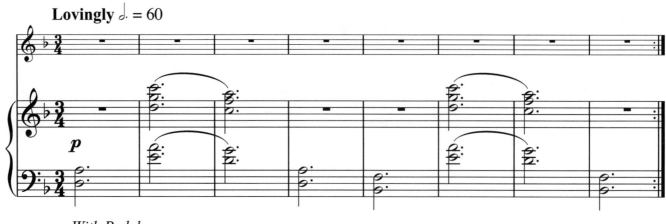

With Pedal

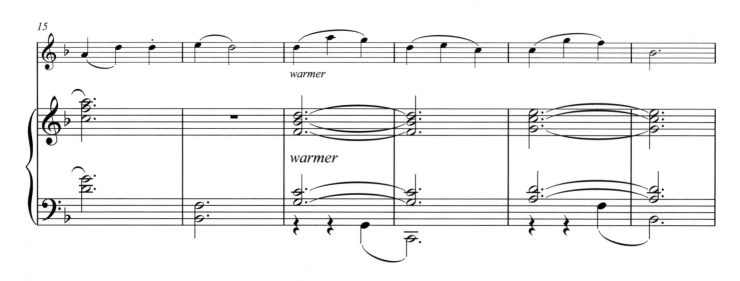

# The Odd Couple

Music by Neal Hefti

# Papageno's Song

from 'The Magic Flute'

Wolfgang Amadeus Mozart

# Sarabande

from 'Solitaire'

Malcolm Arnold
arranged by Alan Poulton

This arrangement is an abridged version of a larger flute and piano arrangement by Alan Poulton
(Order Number NOV954239)

# Somewhere Only We Know

Words & Music by Tim Rice-Oxley,
Tom Chaplin & Richard Hughes

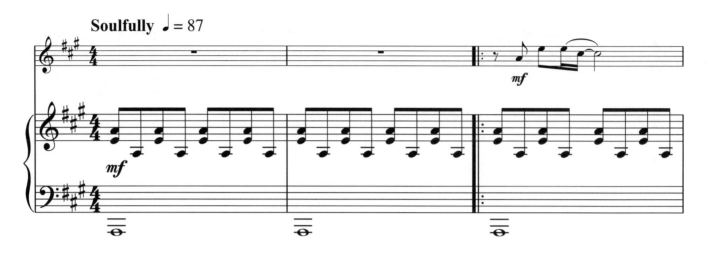

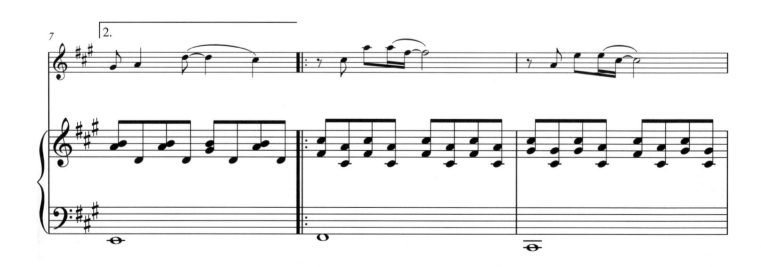

# To A Wild Rose

Music by Edward MacDowell

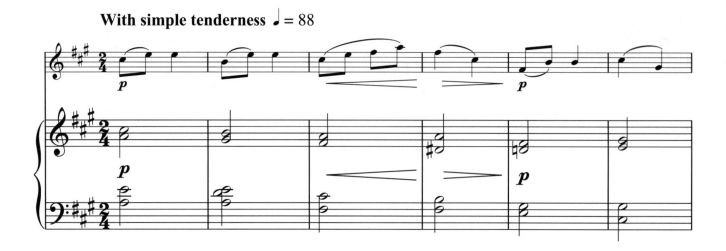

rit.  **D.C. al Coda**  **Coda**

# We Wish You A Merry Christmas

Traditional

**With Yuletide merriment** ♩ = 152

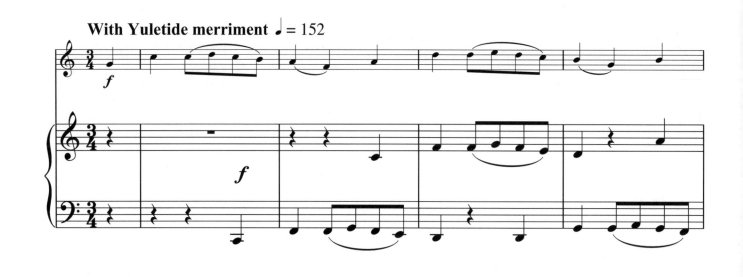

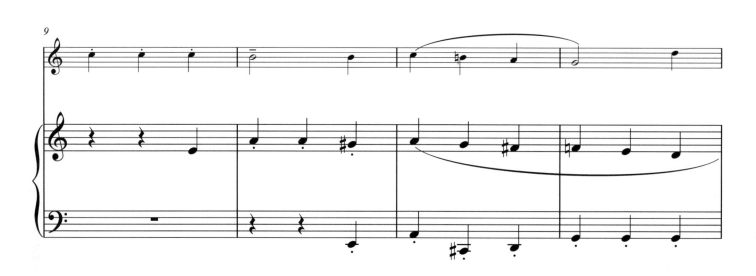

# Pavane

Music by Gabriel Fauré

# LOUISE ENHÖRNING

# AGAPE

"In the garden it had to become apparent to me that I loved Salome. This recognition struck me, since I had not thought it. What a thinker does not think he believes does not exist, and what one who feels does not feel he believes does not exist. You begin to have a presentiment of the whole when you embrace your opposite principle, since the whole belongs to both principles, which grow from one root."

C. G. JUNG

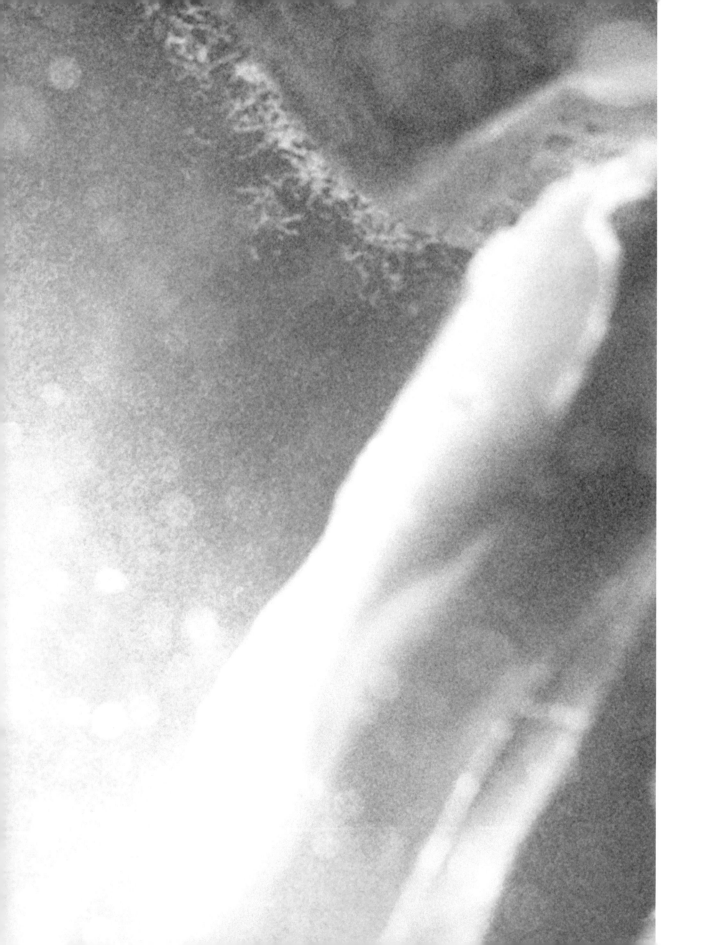

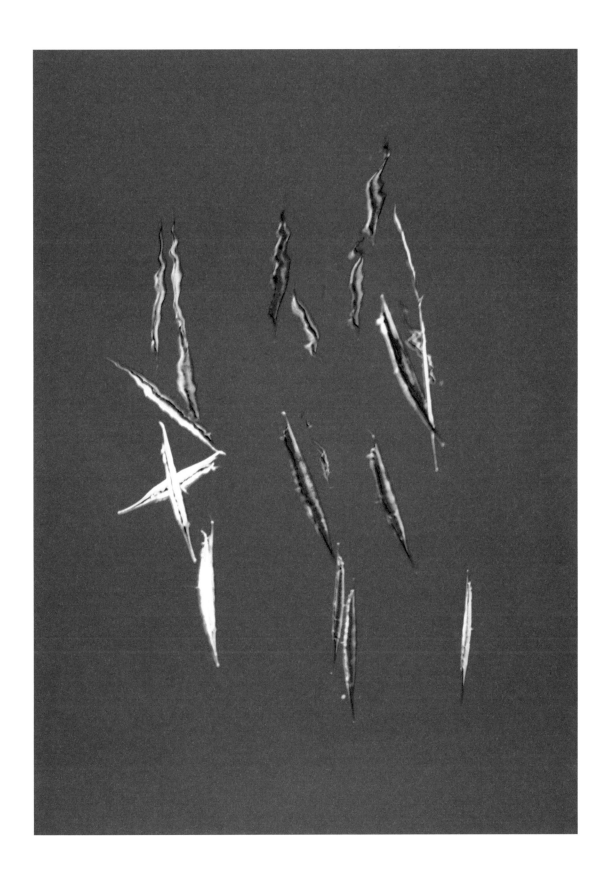

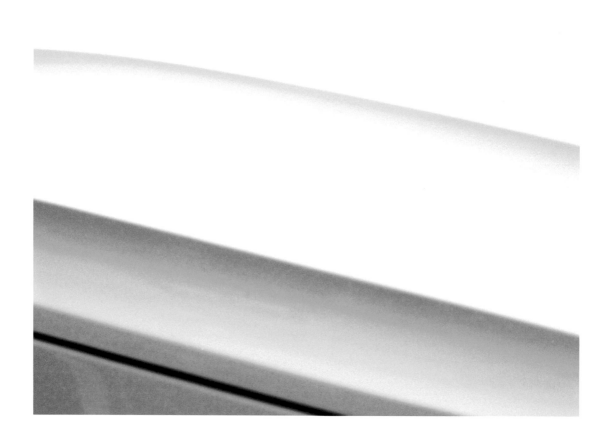

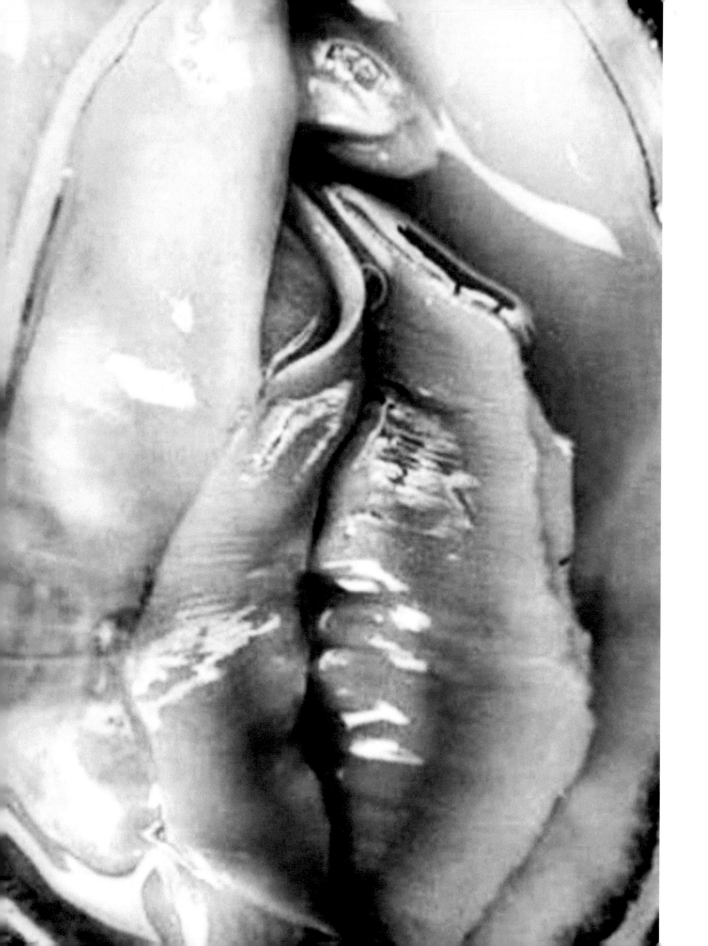

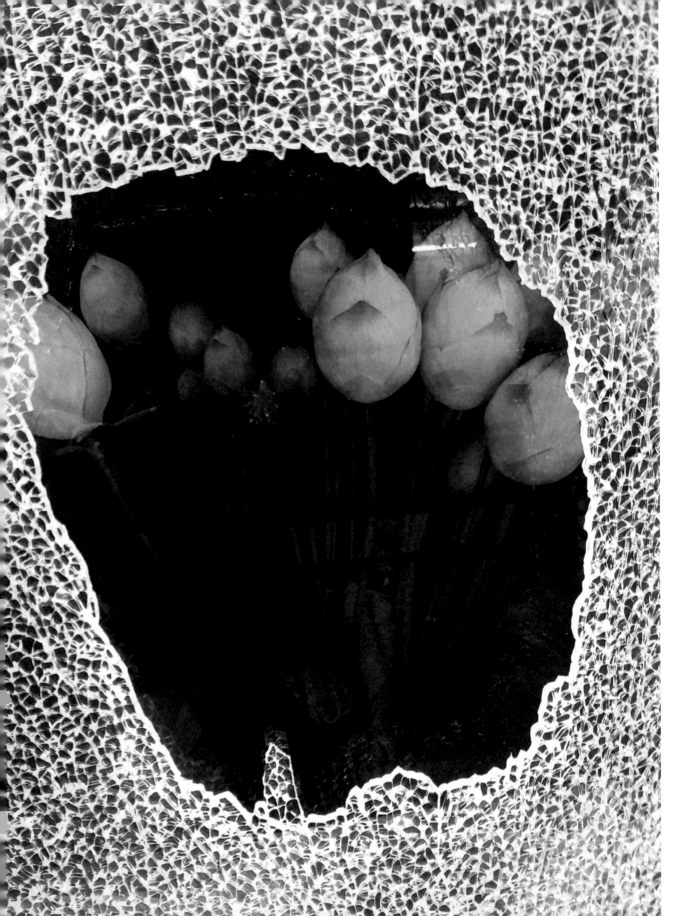

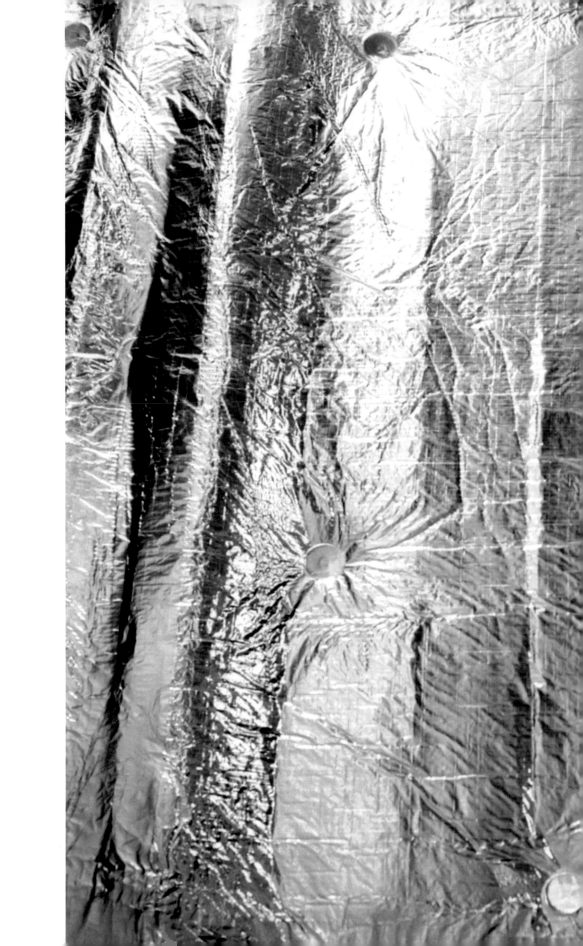

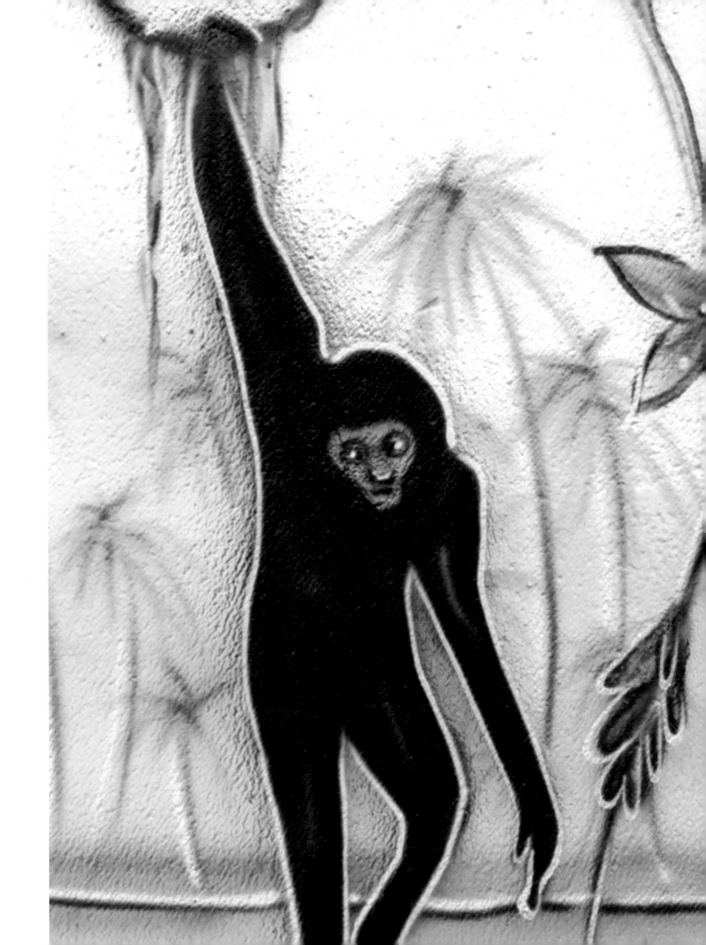

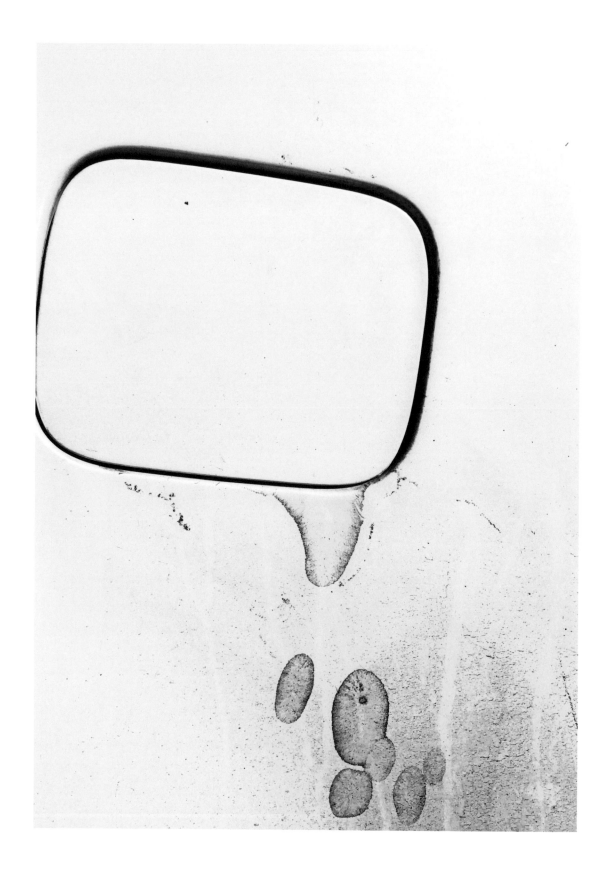

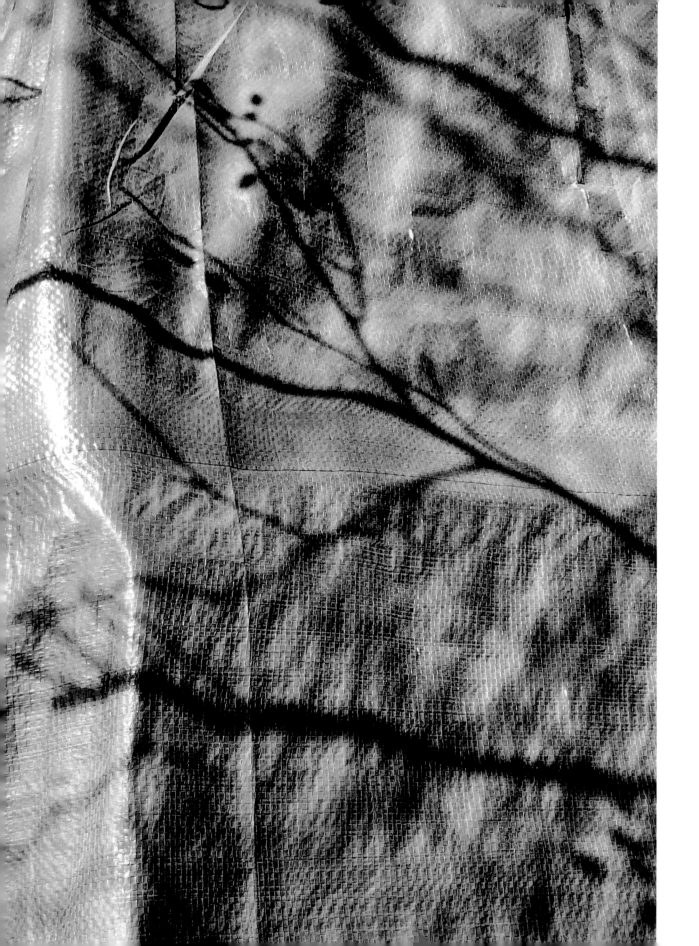

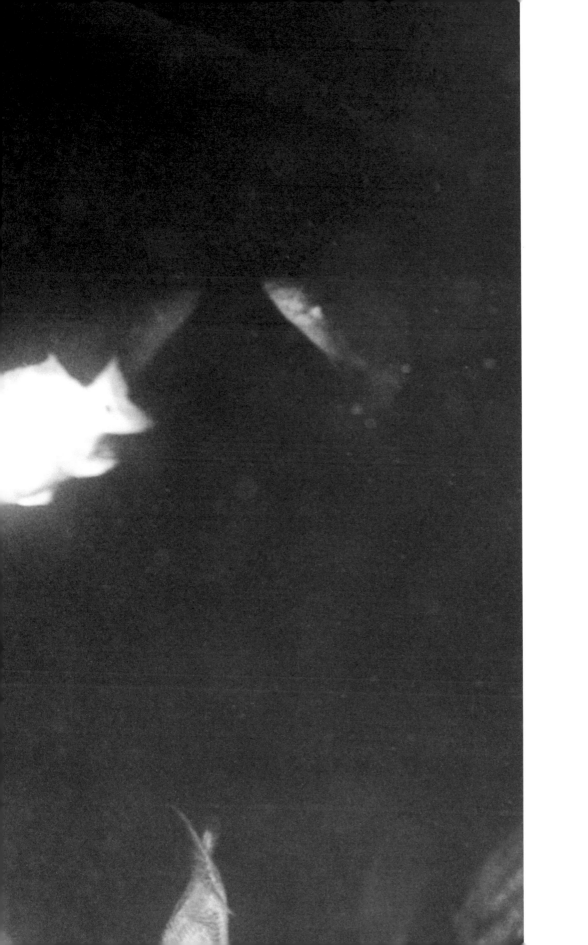

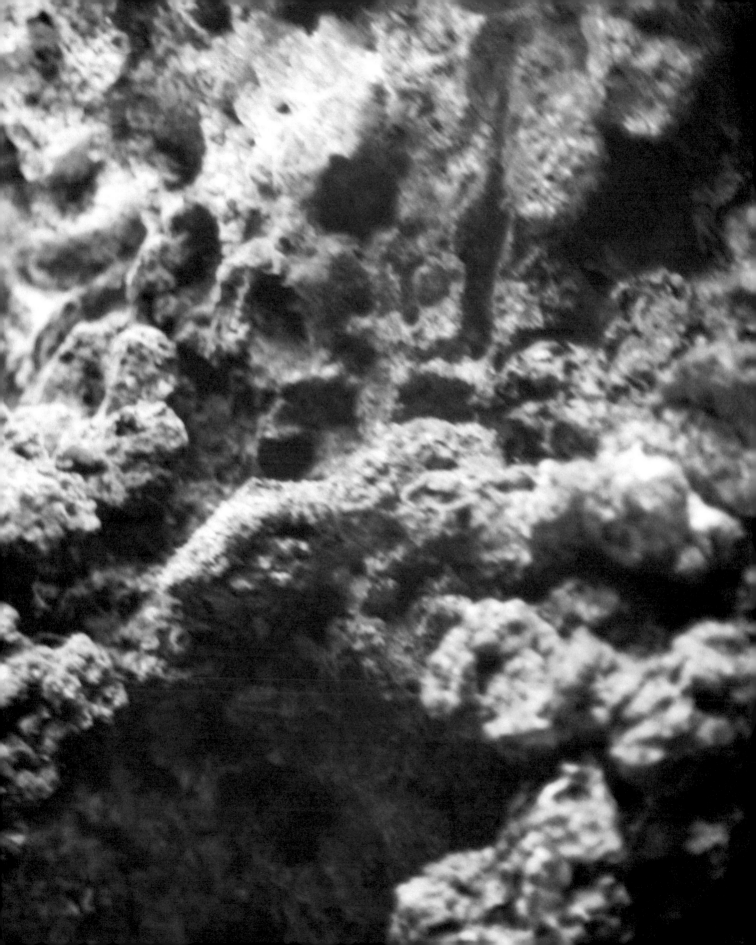

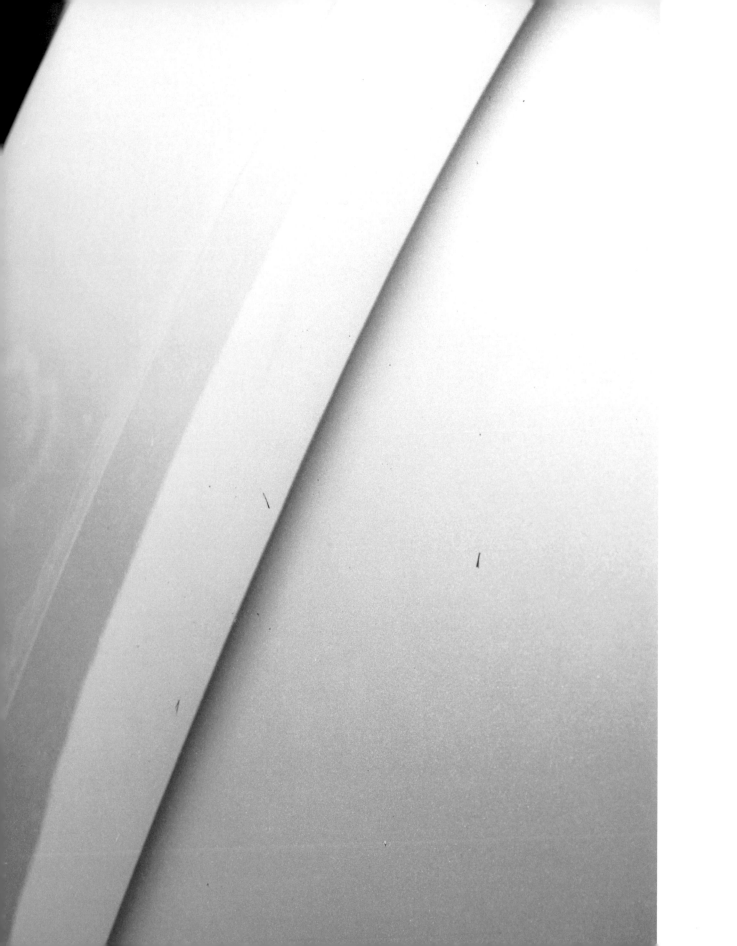

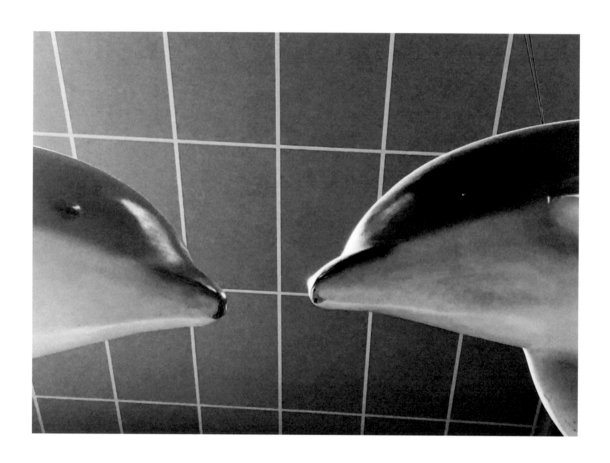

# THIS IS LOVE, YES, YES...

If there is truth to art, it is in the case of Louise Enhörning probably not to be found in what the individual image portrays, but rather in the movement that traverses the whole body of work, which in turn can be sensed in the individual piece. It is the feeling of a movement in thought: "Is that love? Yes, but... " Or maybe rather "Yes, yes, but..." It is an affirmation followed by a confirmation, and a negating modification, simultaneously. There is a rhythm of distance and a lack thereof, in asserting and wondering if that is really all there is to it. As if she was reluctantly seduced by the representations of different kinds of love, and sometimes only interested in hindsight, and only maybe. Love is volatile, sometimes elusive, like clouds; it may appear in a condensed or rarified condition, and as clouds of various kinds: the cumulus clouds of happy days, the altostratus clouds of selfless care, and sometimes it appears in pink, up on cloud nine.

Something seems to have happened to love in recent decades. It no longer appears as a handy solution to social tensions the way it might have during the time of peace, love, and understanding. And although dating apps and Valentine's Day are capitalizing on love in an unprecedented way, people's faith in what is called romantic love seems to be in decline. It is probably not insignificant that Enhörning categorizes a picture of an oyster, which most of all looks like a wet female sex, as "agape." The term has Christian connotations, expressing the idea of an asexual love, like a parent's love for a child, the love of God, or even God's weird love of humankind. Thus, a love that becomes like an atmosphere that you dwell in – all of Enhörning's underwater images are concerned with this kind of love. The oyster picture is indeed a curious choice for the theme, since it is quite an erotic image. I wonder if Enhörning does not reinterpret "agape" here (and possibly even eros) as the love of creative nature (creative love), rather than as altruism in created nature. As if "agape" expresses the creative and generating power of eros, with all the care and attention that an artist shows to his or her work. These underwater visions may portray the deeds of love, the creation of nature, while the images of Walt Disney's films show a love for the created, the boundless love for animals that children can feel, the love of an enchanted world.

In Enhörning's pictures, eroticism is connected to cars, their colors and shapes and the stains that you see on the shiny surfaces. Reflection and fetishism are intermingled in them – sometimes you can see buildings amorphously reflected in them. In the erotic vision, objects of desire are distorted and colored by the reflection, and the distinction between representation and represented is blurred. In the "agape" pictures, however, the object emerges with rather distinct contours against a background that has become so benevolent and supportive that it has almost been dissolved into a soft monochrome. And in the childish representations, everything is produced with black and complete contour lines, as if the objects were distinctively self-sufficient in themselves, without any relations; for that very reason it could be the object of a pure love that doesn't affect the object, nor shape it, but is merely an unusually benevolent medium.

Love and art have traditionally been brought together in the idea of beauty. It is quite possible to see that love has different interpretations. For example, "desire" (Plato) and the elaboration of aesthetics as a discipline, the love that defined the "amateur" (the art lover) was more akin to agape. In the arts today, it is almost considered sentimental to admit to a love of beauty (rather than a preference for the good-looking). If you deal with beauty nowadays, you will inevitably end up close to kitsch. Enhörning does not shy away from this – even pictures of a woman diving naked with a shark beneath her, even pictures of amateurishly painted moonlight breaking through the

clouds have the undeniable, yet unrefined, charm of beauty. Certainly, in love, we inevitably turn into clichés every now and then. The extremely banal side of love. The simple beauty that one must respect even when it is merely symbolized, as in the image of a broken heart, finger-drawn in the grime on a car's tail light, the two pieces of which fit together perfectly (exactly what the ancient Greek word "symbolon" signifies). Enhörning seems to have the capacity, if only for a moment, to both sincerely feel the power of such images and accept it as cringeworthy. It is like every one of her pictures is made twice, in two different moods. There is the sincerity of Jean-Luc Godard, when he has the protagonist in *Breathless* look straight into the camera and say "Si vous n'aimez pas la mer, si vous n'aimez pas la montagne, si vous n'aimez pas la ville... Allez vous faire foutre!" ("If you don't love the sea, if you don't love the mountains, if you don't love the city, go fuck yourself!") There is also Nancy Sinatra's insight, "And then I go and spoil it all by saying something stupid like 'I love you.'" Love is beautiful, yes. Love is ridiculous, yes. This is love, yes, yes, but maybe... Louise Enhörning seems to have done all this through her work, both by surrendering to the banality and beauty of love, but also by the enchantment left behind after the love is gone. I imagine she did it with the pleasure of putting the tip of one's tongue onto a slice of barely ripe lemon. There is always this double movement of receiving, accepting, and refusing, as if there were indeed a time for everything – but also a time that still has to come.

Yes, this is love, but there must be something else there that we are looking for. Perhaps she has embraced the scope of the concept of love that we have inherited from Romanticism? It is much larger than what people seem to mean when they talk about romantic love. In the Romantic world, *eros* and *agape* were united and magnified in a way that enabled the naive and wonderfully simple. A love of everything, that we today meet in the most commercial of children's culture. Romanticism also added a third traditional form of love to it: "philia," friendship. Suddenly, it was possible to imagine that in love, eroticism, friendship, and altruistic love were directed towards the same person, at once. It is indeed a very rich concept of love that Romanticism presented, but I wonder if Enhörning doesn't depart from it regarding the function of this love. Similar to progressive and feminist thinking today, the Romantic thinkers saw a political use for this love: it could be an ideal model for society. I believe that it is here that Enhörning's "yes, yes, but" belongs. Because, even in taking this love as a model for society, love is understood not only as an exception from society, but also as a substitute for it. Love takes care of everything, from economy to morals. It cannot be turned into an institutionalized function of society (devotion, understanding, equality, absolute benevolence, sex, etc.). Of course, yes, yes, society would be a better place if its basic model was love. But that love would still be conceived as a function of society, it would be a socially informed love, only the negative of what society is not. The model for a better society would still be shaped by this very society. But isn't what actually interests us the question of what love would be in a society where equality and brotherhood, peace and understanding, already exist? What is love when it does not have to make up for the shortcomings of society? What is love between two (or more) people who are equal already without love? How would love then appear? What possibilities would it create? If there is truth to art, in the case of this body of work, I believe that it is to be found in this investigation. In something like love's own utopia, in its full potential.

# LARS-ERIK HJERTSTRÖM LAPPALAINEN

# LIST OF WORKS

*Agape* is a metaphor of what love is and can be. It is a series of photographs shot as "self-portraits" from 2016 to 2019.

Transformation 1, May 2018
Agape 1, December 2017
Agape 2, December 2017
Romantic Capitalism 1, November 2017
Transformation 2, April 2019
Eros 1, January 2019
Eros 2, August 2018
Transformation 3, May 2018
Agape 3, February 2017
Agape 4, December 2017
Quiet Heart 2, April 2019
Romantic Capitalism 2, April 2018
Eros 3, April 2018
Romantic Capitalism 3, April 2018
Quiet Heart 4, November 2017
Romantic Capitalism 4, November 2017
Transformation 4, February 2017
Transformation 5, November 2017
Romantic Capitalism 5, November 2017
Quiet Heart 5, August 2018
Quiet Heart 6, April 2018
Transformation 6, November 2017
Agape 5, December 2017
Eros 4, Mars 2017
Romantic Capitalism 6, November 2017
Quiet Heart 7, April 2018
Eros 5, August 2018
Eros 6, August 2018
Quiet Heart 8, April 2018
Eros 7, January 2018
Quiet Heart 9, April 2018
Agape 6, December 2018
Eros 8, April 2018
Romantic Capitalism 7, November 2017
Agape 7, December 2018
Transformation 7, October 2017
Transformation 8, April 2018
Romantic Capitalism 8, November 2017
Agape 8, December 2018
Romantic Capitalism 9, May 2016
Transformation 9, April 2018
Transformation 10, April 2018
Eros 9, Mars 2019
Agape 9, December 2018
Agape 10, December 2018
Romantic Capitalism 10, November 2018
Eros 10, November 2018
Eros 11, September 2016
Eros 12, April 2018
Transformation 11, October 2018
Agape 11, December 2018
Romantic Capitalism 11, November 2018
Romantic Capitalism 12, April 2018

# BIOGRAPHY

Louise Enhörning (b. 1976, Stockholm) is a Swedish artist and photographer based in Stockholm. She holds a degree in Art History from Uppsala University, and has completed courses at Stockholm University and the University of Arts, Crafts, and Design. After finishing her studies, she moved to Paris to pursue a career in photography. She resided in the city for ten years.

In her photographs, she reflects the social mechanisms of our time using her own experience as a point of departure. The sensitive exploration of intimacy involves both an emotional and a physical understanding of her subjects.

Assignments include brands and magazines such as Agnès B, *Dazed and Confused*, Hermès, *Vanity Fair*, and *Vogue*. Photography fine art publications include *Swedish Girls – A Tribute* (Argent Books), *SHOOT – Photography of the Moment* (Rizzoli Publications), and *The Vice Photo Book* (Vice Publications).

Louise Enhörning has had solo exhibitions at Loyal Gallery (Stockholm), Saatchi Office (Stockholm), and OFR Gallery (Paris). Her work has appeared in a number of group shows around the world such as in Barcelona, Copenhagen, Kansas City, Mexico City, New York, and Tokyo. Her public installation *Toys"R"Us* is housed at Malmö Hospital.

Louise Enhörning is represented by LOYAL Gallery, Stockholm.

Graphic Design MAJA KÖLQVIST

Layout CARL VON ARBIN

Printing GÖTEBORGSTRYCKERIET

Paper ARCTIC PAPER, Munken Polar Rough 150 g

Thanks

ALICE SCHULMAN, AMY GIUNTA, ANDERS KLAVENHOLDT, ANNA AHONEN, ANNIKA BERGER, ART AND THEORY, ARCTIC PAPER, BETTINA SCHULTZ, CARL VON ARBIN, DIMEN ABDULLA, ELIN UNNES, FARMOR, HANNA ZELLEKE COLLIN, HANNES HETTA, HENNING HAMILTON, JENS BENSON, JENNY DANIELSSON, JOHN OWEN MARTIN, LARS-ERIK HJERTSTRÖM LAPPALAINEN, LOYAL GALLERY, MAJA KÖLQVIST, MAMMA, MARIE BIRDE, MARTIN FALCK, MARTIN LILJA, MARTIN ROSENGREN, NINA TAHKO, OTTO, PAPPA, PARIS, SILVANA LAGOS, STEFAN FÄLT, SUSANNE ENHÖRNING, VICTORIA BERGSMAN

ISBN 978-91-88031-81-5

Published by

ART AND THEORY PUBLISHING
Erstagatan 26
SE-116 36, Stockholm
www.artandtheory.org

Art and Theory
Publishing